GW00771821

Contents

How to use this guide

Together we will work through all the letters of the Arabic alphabet to make sure that you will be able to recognise the letters and write them yourself.

The first step is to make sure that you are in a comfortable place, away from distractions. You'll need a good pen, too.

To make it more efficient for you, most of the Arabic letters are dealt with in groups. After each explanation, you will find lines to practise writing the letters and words.

Some of the letters sit on the line and some letters reach under the line, just like in the Latin alphabet. This should become clear when you see the Arabic words.

There is enough space for you to practise again at later stages. When you write the words, try to speak them aloud. Revise the letters as often as you can until you feel confident.

HaZZ jayyid
Good luck!

Chapter 1

What you should know in advance

Section 1:   An overview of the alphabet

Writing Arabic is much easier than you would imagine.

Arabic uses an alphabet, not hieroglyphs or pictograms. And there are far fewer shapes to master in Arabic than in those languages that are based on the 'Latin alphabet'.
These distinguish, for example, between capital and small letters as well as between print letters and joined up handwriting.

In Arabic, there is really only **one basic shape for each of the 28 letters** of the alphabet – no capitalization, and not really a distinction between print and handwriting.
Look at the following table, telling you the names of the letters, showing you the shape of each letter and giving you the sound of each letter. Imagine that if there was a line, the first four letters would be sitting on the line, part of the following three letters would be below the line. – Now read the alphabet starting on the right with *alif* being the first letter in the alphabet and *yaa'* being the last.

raa'	dhal	daal	khaa'	Haa'	jeem	thaa'	taa'	baa'	alif
ر	ذ	د	خ	ح	ج	ث	ت	ب	أ
r	dh	d	kh	H	j	th	t	b	a

faa'	ghain	3ayn	Zaa'	Taa'	Daad	Saad	sheen	seen	zay
ف	غ	ع	ظ	ط	ض	ص	ش	س	ز
f	gh	3	Z	T	D	S	sh	s	z

		yaa'	waw	haa'	nuun	meem	laam	kaaf	qaaf
		ي	و	ه	ن	م	ل	ك	ق
		y	w	h	n	m	l	k	q

Section 2:   Three important technicalities

Writing from right to left
In many ways it is a more natural movement to be pushing the pen than pulling it, certainly for someone who is right-handed. And if you are left-handed, Arabic is the language for you: You will never smudge your paper again.

However, for both left-handers and right-handers the basics are the same.

Holding the pen
Even if you have bad handwriting in your own language, there is no reason why your Arabic handwriting should not be excellent. You are starting afresh with good habits from the start. Firstly, to hold the pen you must have **finger-tip control**. It is better to hold the pen or pencil with the fingers well away from the point.

Flexibility of the wrist
This is something that textbooks never tell you:
The basic movement in writing Arabic is making **clockwise loops.**
Try it: Start making clockwise loops **from right to left** on the lines below. Be careful to write two-thirds of the loop above and one third below the line.

You can practise this movement at any time when you are free and have pen and paper to hand. You will find it to be very natural after only a short time.

Section 3: First attempts at writing Arabic words

Joining or not joining letters

Look at the three words in the first line of the table. The first word on the right has all its letters joined up. The next word has some letters joined up. The third consists of individual letters only, which are not joined up.

وَرْد	فول	قَلْب
و ر د	ف و ل	ق ل ب
d r w	l uu f	b l q
ward	fuul	qalb
roses	foul	heart

As you can see from this table, some letters in the Arabic language are joined up with other letters, and some letters are not joined up.

About consonants and vowels

Before we proceed, have another look at the table above. It shows you that you only write the consonants and long vowels of words. Examples of words written with consonants only are *qalb* (*qaaf - laam - baa'*) and *ward* (*waw - raa' - daal*).

An example of a word with a long vowel is *fuul* written *faa' - waw - laam*.

Don't be confused by the fact that *waw* is seen as a consonant at the beginning of a word and as a long vowel in the middle of a word.

Chapter 2

'Non-joiners', the *hamza* & additional help symbols

Section 1: The six 'non-joiners' in the Arabic alphabet

As you now already know, some letters are not joined up in Arabic writing. All in all there are **six so-called 'non-joiners'.** These are letters that are never joined to another letter on the left. They are:

و	ز	ر	ذ	د	أ
waw	zay	raa'	dhal	daal	alif

Try writing the six Arabic letters, the first three sitting on the line, the next three reaching partly below the line. – Remember to write from right to left and to start the letters at the top.

There is a short video on YouTube, created by Pendragon Educational Publishers, called "How to write the Arabic alphabet + free worksheet (slow version)" that gives you an idea and some help how you should best write. The link is given below. Refer to this as often as you can.

http://youtu.be/mFxNkgC-Txo

Or type these keywords into YouTube: "*Student learning to write the Arabic alphabet*".

Now look at some more words consisting of non-joiners only.
Try to practise writing them as neatly as you can.
Start each word on the right, beginning with each letter at the top. Also pay attention where
you place the letters: Some sit on the line, others start above the line and end below the line.

زِرّ	رُزّ	دار	رادار
rr z	zz r	r aa d	r aa d aa r
zirr	ruzz	daar	raadaar
button	rice	house, home	radar

You should notice that it isn't all that difficult to write Arabic.
With only six letters you have already been able to write some useful words.

Section 2:   The *hamza* (ء) – a 'letter' that doesn't appear in the alphabet

hamza is the name of the symbol in brackets in the title of this section.
The *hamza* can be found in connection with three letters:

ؤ	ئ	أ
waw + *hamza*	yaa' + *hamza*	alif + *hamza*

Try to write these three letters with the *hamza*.

Remember the 'clockwise loops': Write the body of each letter beginning at the top on the right and add the *hamza* last. You will now see that part of the last two letters has to go below the line.

_____

_____

_____

_____

_____

_____

The *hamza* in connection with the letter *alif*

Perhaps you have already noticed that the *alif* at the beginning of a word practically always appears with a *hamza* – and the *hamza* can be in two different places. Have a look:

إِسْلام	أُمّ	أَب
islaam	umm	ab
hamza **below** the *alif*	*hamza* **above** the *alif*	*hamza* **above** the *alif*

You can see from the table that each of the words starts with a different vowel /a/, /u/, /i/, although each of the words has an *alif* at the beginning.

In the first two words from the right, the *hamza* is above the *alif*. In this case you read the *alif* as /a/ or /u/.

Only the context in which a word appears tells you what sound you must read. At first this may seem very difficult for beginners. But relax. We'll work through this together as we go along.

When the *hamza* is below the *alif* – as in *islaam* (see above) – it must be read as /i/.

Always remember: All words in Arabic that begin with a vowel have *alif* (often with a *hamza* and an additional help symbol) as their first letter.

_____

_____

_____

_____

Section 3: Additional help symbols with *alif*

Look at this table. Additional symbols have been added.

إِسْلام	أُمّ	أَب
islaam	umm	ab
hamza + additional symbol **below** the *alif*	*hamza* + additional symbol **above** the *alif*	*hamza* + additional symbol **above** the *alif*

These additional symbols are used in the Arab world in children's books, in textbooks in primary school, in books for learners of Arabic and also in the Holy Koran. And here is what they mean:

In the first word on the right the *hamza* and the other little symbol above the *hamza* tell you that the *alif* must be read as /a/. (The technical term for this additional symbol is *fatHa.* It always marks a short /a/.)

In the word in the middle the *hamza* and the other little symbol above the *hamza* tell you that the *alif* must be read as /u/. This symbol, if you look at it closely, looks like the 'small brother' of the letter *waw*. (The technical term for this additional symbol is *Damma.* It always marks a short /u/.)

In the word on the left the *hamza* and the other little symbol below the *hamza* tell you that the *alif* must be read as /i/. (The technical term for this additional symbol is *kasra.* It always marks a short /i/.)

And now try this task – it may be quite difficult to begin with: Practise writing the three words above with the additional symbols. It may help you to say the words as you are writing them.

Remember: Write in clockwise loops.
Write from right to left.
Start with the body of *alif* at the top.
Be careful: The dot in the first word and parts of the second and third word must go below the line.
Add the *hamza* and the help symbol after writing the 'body' of the *alif*.

And here is tip:

There are only very few words where the *alif* does not have a *hamza* at the beginning of the word. You may know two of these words:

اِسْم	اِبْن
ism	ibn
name	son

Try to write them.

_____

_____

Chapter 3

The five 'boat' letters

Section 1:   Row, row, row the boat …

The next three letters that you will learn to write all look a little bit like a boat:

ث	ت	ب
thaa'	taa'	baa'

As you can see, the three letters are identical in their 'body' (= the boat). The difference arises from the dots below and above the boat.

Let's focus on *baa'* to show how this letter is written in different places of a word. You will soon notice that the writing isn't very difficult at all. Have a look:

at the end	in the middle	at the beginning	on its own
ـب	ـبـ	بـ	ب
قَلْب	تِبْن	بابا	أب
qalb	tibn	baabaa	ab
heart	straw	daddy	father

Notice the help symbols in three of the words. The little symbol above the letters *alif* and *qaaf* tells you that you must read /a/. The symbol below the letter *taa'* tells you that you must read /i/.

Now give it a go. Start practising: As you are writing, slowly say and join the letters that you are writing.

Now you have mastered the letter *baa'*, you will find it quite easy to write the following eight words with the letters *taa'* and *thaa'*. They are in two sets of four.

at the end	in the middle	at the beginning	on its own
ـت	ـتـ	تـ	ت
بِنْـت	زَوجَتـي	تِـبْـن	توت
bint	zawjatee	tibn	tuut
daughter	my wife	straw	berries

at the end	in the middle	at the beginning	on its own
ثـ	ـثـ	ثـ	ث
بَحَـث	كَـثـير	ثَـوْب	ثَلاث
baHath	katheer	thawb	thalaath
research	many, much	clothes	three

Section 2:   A boat or not a boat? – That is the question.

We will now turn to two more letters which, when on their own, are only vaguely similar in shape to the 'boat'-letters. These two letters are:

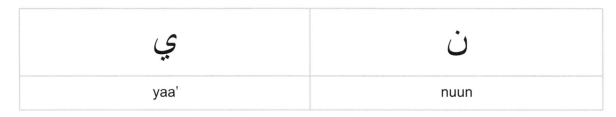

ي	ن
yaa'	nuun

Now look what happens to their shape when *nuun* and *yaa'* are used in different places in a word.

at the end	in the middle	at the beginning	on its own
ـن	ـنـ	نـ	ن
مَـن	فِنْجان	نَوْم	فِنْجان
man	finjaan	nawm	finjaan
who	cup	sleep (= noun)	cup

Now practise writing the letter and words with the letter *nuun*. – Remember that the *nuun* reaches below the line when it has a 'belly'.

_____

_____

_____

_____

at the end	in the middle	at the beginning	on its own
ـي	ـيـ	يـ	ي
بَيْتِي	بَـيْـتِي	يَوْم	شاي
baytee	baytee	yawm	shaay
my house	my house	day	tea

It will not be difficult for you to detect that *nuun* and *yaa'* are written as you find them in the alphabet when used on their own or at the end of a word.
However, when used at the beginning of a word or in the middle of a word, their shape is identical to that of the 'boat'-letters. They simply differ in the number and the place of the dots.

It is time again for you to practise your handwriting. Now write the words with the letter *yaa'*. *Hayya bina!*

Section 3: Test yourself – Identifying letters.

How many times can you find the letters *yaa', taa', nuun, baa', thaa'*?

ث	ـت	ن	ي	ثـ
ب	ت	ي	ـنـ	ـب
ـن	ـيـ	ثـ	يـ	ـبـ
تـ	ـبـ	ـتـ	ن	ـنـ
ثـ	ـتـ	ـب	يـ	ـت

yaa' _____ times

taa' _____ times

thaa' _____ times

nuun _____ times

baa' _____ times

Here is the solution:

Chapter 4

How to turn 'grandad' into 'limit' and 'cheek'

21

Section 1:   The dot that makes the difference

You might well ask what this means: How can you turn 'grandad' into 'limit' and 'cheek'?
Well, in Arabic that's quite easy. But first look at this table.

خ	ح	ج
khaa'	Haa'	jeem

As you can see, these three letters all have the same shape. The only difference between them is the presence or absence or the place of the dot. Try to write these three letters: Begin each letter at the top on the left, go a little to the right and 'draw' a semicircle, this time anti-clockwise. Finally add the dot where necessary.

Word morph

Now we will turn the word 'grandad' into 'limit/border' and 'cheek'. Look at these three words in which the three letters appear at the beginning of the word.

خدّ	حدّ	جدّ
khadd	**H**add	**j**add
cheek	limit, border	grandad

The tricky bit here is to know very well where the dots go or don't go.
If you are not careful with the dots, you will turn your grandad into a border or a cheek.
Practise writing the words.

Section 2:   Changes in shape according to place

And here you have three tables where you can see how the three letters change according to their places in a word. Try to write the following words with the letters *jeem, Haa'* and *khaa'*.

jeem

at the end	in the middle	at the beginning	on its own
جـ	ـجـ	جـ	ج
ثَلْجٌ	فِنْجان	جَدّ	تاج
thalj	finjaan	jadd	taaj
snow	cup	grandad	crown

_____

_____

_____

_____

_____

Haa'

at the end	in the middle	at the beginning	on its own
ح	ح	ح	ح
سَبَحَ	بَحْر	حَدّ	تُفاح
sabaH	baHr	Hadd	tufaaH
he swam	sea	limit, border	apple

_____

_____

_____

_____

khaa'

at the end	in the middle	at the beginning	on its own
ـخ	ـخـ	خـ	خ
بَطّيـخ	تَخْـت	خَدّ	خَوْخ
baTTeekh	takht	khadd	khawkh
watermelon	bed	cheek	plum

Chapter 5

'Non-identical twins' (1): The letters *seen* and *sheen*

Section 1:   Three dots that make the difference

Have a good look at the next two letters.

ش	س
sheen	seen

Again, we have 'twins' here, but obviously not identical twins. The body of both letters is identical, but the letter *sheen* additionally has three dots.

Before you have a look at how these two letters are written in words, try to write them on their own several times to get a feel for both letters. Their 'bellies' should reach below the line. – As always, the dots should be added last.

Section 2:   Relaxing in the sun on a ship, perhaps

Now for something more difficult: Here you can see the letter *seen* as it is used in four different words.

at the end	in the middle	at the beginning	on its own
ـس ــس	ــسـ ــ	سـ ــ	س
شـــمـــس	عـــسـَـل	سَـفينة	دَرْس
shams	3asal	safeena	dars
sun	honey	ship	lesson, unit

Try to write the four words, each of them several times to get used to moving your pen clockwise.

When you have mastered the *dars*, you can afford to relax in the *shams* on a *safeena*.

Section 3: The sun, a bed and a treat of apricots

And now for the letter *sheen*.

Look, see how the letters change in the same way as *seen*, and then give it a go and write the four words several times. – As a reward you will be allowed to relax on a *firaash* in the *shams* and have *mishmish* as a snack.

at the end	in the middle	at the beginning	on its own
ـش	ـشـ	شـ	ش
ريـْش	مِـشْـمِـش	شَـمْـس	فِراش
reesh	mishmish	shams	firaash
feather	apricots	sun	bed, mattress

_____

_____

_____

_____

_____

_____

Chapter 6

'Non-identical twins' (2): The letters *Saad* and *Daad*

Section 1:   How to write the letters *Saad* and *Daad*

You will by now know that quite a few letters in the Arabic alphabet only differ through the presence and absence of dots and the number of dots. This is again the case with the letters *Saad* and *Daad*.

Additionally, you will notice that the 'end part', i.e. the part on the left of the two letters (almost looking like a tub) is the same as in the letters *seen* and *sheen*.

When you want to write these *Saad* and *Daad*, start at the point before the 'tub' and write a clockwise loop. When you get to the end of the loop, lead your pencil upwards a little bit and then, clockwise, finish the letter with the 'tub'.

Practise writing the two letters to keep your wrist flexible.

ض	ص
Daad	Saad

Section 2: The letter *Saad* – changes in shape according to place

Here you can see how *Saad* is used in four words. Write them several times.

at the end	in the middle	at the beginning	on its own
ـص	ـصـ	صـ	ص
مِقَصّ	نِصْف	صَديق	باص
miqaSS	niSf	Sadeeq	baaS
scissors	half	friend	bus

Section 3: The letter *Daad* – changes in shape according to place

Perhaps you have heard that the following letter, *Daad,* is very special.

Arabic is sometimes even called 'the language of the *Daad*'.

Some people say that this sound, if spoken properly, only exists in Arabic. – Now try to write the following four words.

at the end	in the middle	at the beginning	on its own
ـض	ـضـ	ضـ	ض
مَريـض	مَضْـرِب	ضَـيْف	أَرْض
mareeD	maDrib	Dayf	arD
ill, sick	bat, racket	guest	floor, ground

_____

_____

_____

_____

_____

Chapter 7

Revision of the letters dealt with so far

A guide to writing Arabic

Look at this table and first of all try to identify the letters in the right column. What are their names? – Now try to write the words by joining the letters. (Of course you can go back and look at how the letters must be written in different places of a word.) Say the letters as you are writing them and finally try to say each word.

word	single letters
patience	ر + ب + ص
molar	س + ر + ض
window, glass	ج + ا + ج + ز
magic	ر + ح + س
curtain	ر + ا + ت + س
tea	ي + ا + ش

If your words look a little bit like these, you have done a really good job.

word	single letters
صَبْر	ص + ب + ر
ضِرْس	ض + ر + س
زُجاج	ز + ج + ا + ج
سِحْر	س + ح + ر
سِتار	س + ت + ا + ر
شاي	ش + ا + ي

Now practise writing the words again.

_____

_____

_____

_____

_____

_____

Chapter 8

From medicine to zoology

Section 1:   The letters *Taa'* and *Zaa'*

In Arabic, you can easily mix up something medicinal with an animal that you might meet in the woods. – If you look at the Arabic script of the following two words (both are written without any help symbols), you will see why this is the case. Try to identify the only difference between the two words.

ظبي	طبي
Zabee	Tibbiyy
a deer	medicinal

Now look at the initial letters of the two words.

ظ	ط
Zaa'	Taa'

Write them several times until you have got used to them.

_____

_____

_____

_____

_____

Section 2:   The letter *Taa'* – changes in shape according to place

Now look at how the individual letter remains or stays the same in different places in a word. Then practise writing these words.

at the end	in the middle	at the beginning	on its own
ط	ط	ط	ط
بَطّ	شَنْطَة	طَبِيب	شُبَّاط
baTT	shanTa	Tabeeb	shubbaaT
duck	bag, suitcase	doctor	February

Section 3:   The letter *Zaa'* – changes in shape according to place

And now look at the table for the letter *Zaa*:

at the end	in the middle	at the beginning	on its own
ـظـ	ـظـ	ـظـ	ظ
حَــظّ	نَــظّــارة	ظَــبي	حِفاظ
HaZZ	naZZara	Zabee	HifaaZ
luck	glasses	a deer	upkeep, conservation

Try it yourself: Practise writing the words.
HaZZ jayyid – Good luck.

_____

_____

_____

_____

_____

Chapter 9

The letters *3ayn* and *ghain*

41

Section 1: The number 3 inverted

If you take a mirror and hold it in such a way that you can see these two letters in the mirror, you will see that both the letter *3ayn* and the letter *ghain* look a little bit like the number 3 inverted and written by a pre-school child.

Practise writing these two letters. Remember to relax your wrist and to start at the top. Then go below the line with the bottom part of the letters. – Notice that they are two of the few letters that are written anti-clockwise.

غ	ع
ghain	3ayn

The two tables in the next section show you what these letters look like when used within words in different places.

Look from right to left, beginning with the first column on the right.

When you have decoded the words, practise writing them.

Section 2:   The letter *3ayn* – changes in shape according to place

Here is the table for the letter *3ayn*:

at the end	in the middle	at the beginning	on its own
ـع	ـعـ	عـ	ع
سَريـع	سَـعـيد	عَـيْن	شارِع
saree3	sa3eed	3ayn	shaari3
fast, quick	happy	spring, eye	street

_____

_____

_____

_____

_____

Section 3: The letter *ghain* – changes in shape according to place

Here is the table for the letter *ghain*:

at the end	in the middle	at the beginning	on its own
ـغ	ـغـ	غـ	غ
مَبْلَغ	صَغـير	غـابة	فَراغ
mablagh	Sagheer	ghaaba	faraagh
amount, sum	small, little	woods	gap

You will know by now that only practice makes perfect (*at-tikraar yu3allim al-Himaar*). Practise writing the words from the table.

After you have done that, you can go for a walk in the *ghaaba* again, watch out and try to find an *3ayn Sagheer* that can make you *sa3eed*.

_____

_____

_____

_____

_____

Chapter 10

The letters *faa'* and *qaaf*

45

Section 1: Meeting a friend for a cup of coffee

The following two letters only show some similarity when looked at on their own.

ق	ف
qaaf	faa'

However, as the following two tables show, with the exception of the number of dots they are identical in two places: when they are at the beginning of a word and when they are in the middle of a word.

at the end	in the middle	at the beginning	on its own
ـف	ـفـ	فـ	ف
أَلْـف	تَـفَـضّـل	فِنْجان	رَفّ
alf	tafaDDal	finjaan	raff
one thousand	Here you are.	cup	shelf

at the end	in the middle	at the beginning	on its own
ـق	ـقـ	قـ	ق
صَدِيـق	مَقْـهى	قَـهْوة	سوق
Sadeeq	maqha	qahwa	suuq
friend	café	coffee	bazar, souk

Take your time and slowly 'draw' the words first. Then see if you can also write them a little faster. After you have finished, you may go to the *suuq*, meet a *Sadeeq* and have a *finjaan qahwa* in a little nice *maqha*.

_____

_____

_____

_____

_____

Chapter 11

Odds and ends

Section 1:   The letter *kaaf*

We are nearing the end of the alphabet. So far we have covered 24 of the 28 letters in the Arabic alphabet. The following four letters can't be grouped in any way, so let's have a look at them, each individually.

The first of these letters is *kaaf*. Look at this table to see how it is written in different places in a word. Then again take a piece of paper and practise writing the four words.

at the end	in the middle	at the beginning	on its own
ـك	ـكـ	كـ	ك
سَمَـك	سِكّينة	كِتاب	شُبّاك
samak	sikkeena	kitaab	shubbaak
fish	knife	book	window

Section 2: The letter *laam*

The second letter from the odds-and-ends group is the letter *laam*.
Look at these four food words. They all contain this letter.

at the end	in the middle	at the beginning	on its own
ـلـ	ـلـ	ـل	ل
فَلافِـل	سَـلَـطة	لَـبَن	فول
falaafill	salaTa	laban	fuul
falafel	salad	yogurt	foul

… but don't think that *laam* only exists in words to do with food.

You can also find the letter *laam* in the words *qalb* (heart), *kalb* (dog), *balad* (country), *Huluu* (sweet).

_____

_____

_____

_____

_____

_____

Section 3:   The letter combinations of *laam* and *alif*

Before we move on to the next letter, you must know two special things about the letter combination *laam + alif*.

First: Please have a look at the following two words. In each case the *laam* is joined up from the right and followed by the *alif*.

Pay attention to the way this letter combination is written. Then practise yourself.

سَـــلام	فَـــلافِل
salaam	falaafil
peace	falafel

To make it quite clear, see what happens when the individual letters are joined up in the word *salaam*:

$$ س + ل + ا + م = سَـــلام $$

Second: There are, of course, also words where the *laam* is **not** joined up from the right. Have a look:

الأب	لا
al-ab	la
the father	no

As you can see, the combination *laam + alif* is again written in a different way.

The table below shows you again what form this letter combination takes.

$$لا = 1 + ل$$

Don't forget to practise writing the letter and all the words with *laam* before you have a look at the letter *meem*.

Section 4: The letter *meem*

at the end	in the middle	at the beginning	on its own
ـم	ـمـ	مـ	م
قَلَـم	حَمـامة	مَوْز	حَمّـام
qalam	Hamaama	mawz	Hammaam
pen, pencil	pigeon	bananas	bathroom

Now practise writing the *meem* words.

_____

_____

_____

_____

_____

Section 5:   The letter *haa'*

You have now reached the last of the 28 letters. It is the letter *haa'*.
Practise writing this letter and the four words in the table.

at the end	in the middle	at the beginning	on its own
ـه	ـهـ	هـ	ه
وَجْه	مِهْنة	هَدِيّة	أبوه
wajh	mihna	hadiyya	abuuhu
face	profession	present (= noun)	his father

Congratulations. You have actually worked your way through the complete Arabic alphabet and practised writing a few words for each of the 28 letters.

_____

_____

_____

_____

_____

Chapter 12

And finally …

Section 1: Another two letters that are not in the alphabet

There are two more letters that are not in the alphabet. They are the *ta'marbuTa* and the *alif maksuura*. Here is a table with two words that both end on almost the same sound.

مُسْتَشْفـى	سَيَّارة
mustash**fa**	sayyaa**ra**
hospital	car

As you can see, the sounds are expressed through two different letters that you don't find in the alphabet. Let us first look at the letter at the end of the word *sayyaara*. It looks like the letter *haa'* with two dots on it. Its name is *ta'marbuTa*.
Whenever feminine forms of a word are made out of the masculine forms, then these feminine forms have a *ta'marbuTa* at the end. Look at the following table.

	feminine forms		masculine forms
Tabeeba doctor	طَبيبة	Tabeeb doctor	طَبيب
kabeera big, old	كَبيرة	kabeer big, old	كَبير
ibna daughter	اِبْنة	ibn son	اِبْن
qiTTa (female) cat	قِطّة	qiTT (male) cat / tomcat	قِطّ

Let us now look at the end of the word *mustashfa* (hospital). Although the last sound is nearly the same as in *sayyaara* (car), it is written in a different way. If you look carefully, you will see that this letter looks like the letter *yaa'* without the dots. Its name is *alif maksuura*.

muuseeqa music	موسيقــى
ila to	إلــى
3ala on, at	عَلــى
ishtara he bought	اِشْتَرى
yansa he forgets	يَنْســى
SaHaara deserts	صَحارى
baka he cried	بَكــى
atamanna lak iqaama jameela. I wish you a pleasant stay.	أَتَمَنّــى لَك إقامة جَميلة

Practise writing the words.

_____

_____

_____

_____

_____

Chapter 13

Two activities

Section 1:   Recognising letters

To have a good knowledge of Arabic letters is a precondition for reading and writing. That's why you should do the following activity.

Now find the letters *haa'* and *meem* in the following table. Mark the letters in different colours. – Be careful, in two of the words you will find both *meem* and *haa'*.

hello	مَرْحَباً
word	كَلِمة
Hadi	هادي
welcome	أَهْلاً وَسَهْلاً
computer	كُمْبْيوتِر
engineer	مُهَنْدِس
day	يَوْم
interest	اِهْتِمام

The solutions are on the next page.

Solutions

hello	مَرْحَباً
word	كَلِمة
Hadi	هـادي
welcome	أَهْـلاً وَسَـهْـلاً
computer	كُمْبْيوتِر
engineer	مُـهَنْدِس
day	يَوم
interest	اِهْـتِـمـام

Section 2: Joining up letters

As letters have slightly different shapes in different places in a word, the following activity will help you to practise 'joined-up' writing.

Look at all the different kinds of single letters, read them in order to see what word you should write, and finally join up the single letters and give them their 'right' shape. Write the joined up words, using the lines beneath the letters. Remember to write below the lines where necessary.

garden	ح + د + ي + ق + ة
Come!	ت + ع + ا + ل
Agreed.	ق + ف + ا + و + م
great	ع + ظ + ي + م

word	single letters
diarrhoea	ل + ا + ه + س + إ
breakfast	ر + و + ط + ف
stuffed	ت + ا + ي + ش + ح + م
evening	ء + ا + س + م

The solutions are on the next page.

Solutions

joined up word	single letters
حَديقة	ح + د + ي + ق + ة =
تَعال	ت + ع + ا + ل =
مُوافِق	م + و + ا + ف + ق =
عَظيم	ع + ظ + ي + م =
إسْهال	إ + س + ه + ا + ل =
فُطور	ف + ط + و + ر =
مَحْشيات	م + ح + ش + ي + ا + ت =
مَساء	م + س + ا + ء =

When you have come to this point, you might feel you have climbed Mount Everest.

And what you might say at this point is a phrase that you have come across many times to express great relief: *al-Hamdu lillah*.

If you'd like to continue learning Arabic, visit our website at: www.arabiconline.eu

If you found this book helpful, please leave positive feedback on web stores, social networks, or write to info@pendragoned.co.uk.

As you have now reached the end of this book, all that remains to say is:

mabruuk

Congratulations!

Use this space for making notes and further practice.